3 Transpose this melody *up* an octave, using the treble clef as shown.

10

Marcello

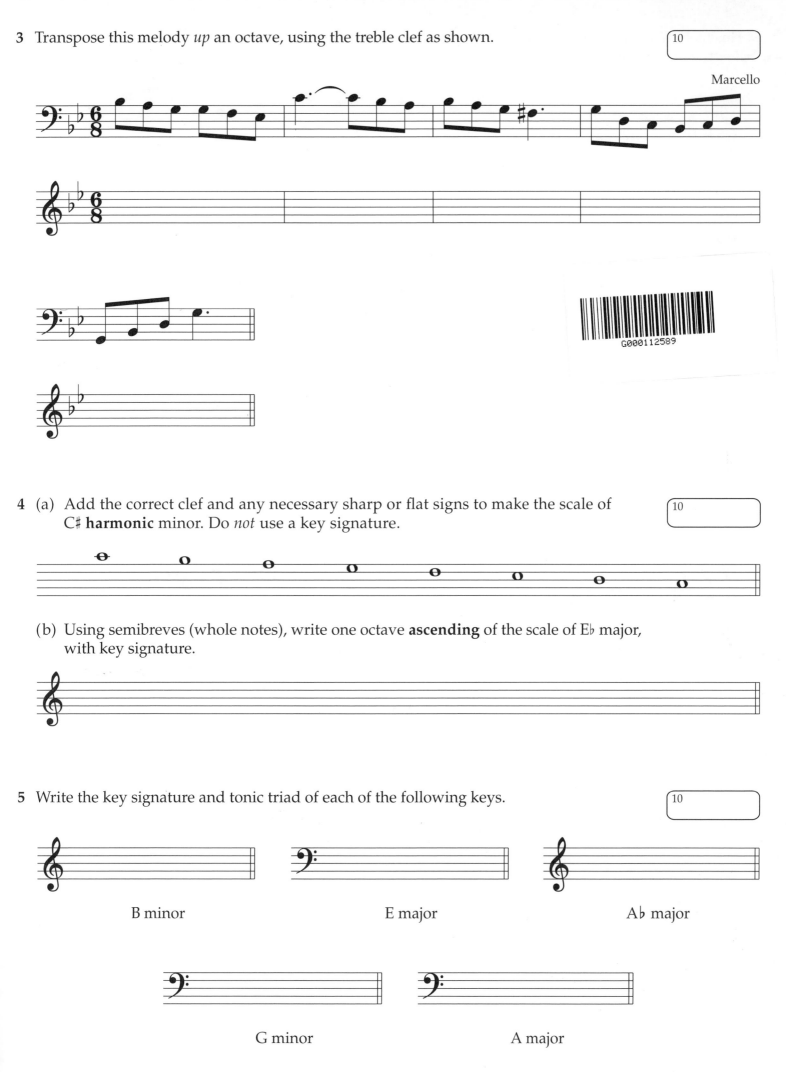

4 (a) Add the correct clef and any necessary sharp or flat signs to make the scale of C♯ **harmonic** minor. Do *not* use a key signature.

10

(b) Using semibreves (whole notes), write one octave **ascending** of the scale of E♭ major, with key signature.

5 Write the key signature and tonic triad of each of the following keys.

10

B minor   E major   A♭ major

G minor   A major

3

6 This melody, adapted from a piece by Haydn, contains *five* deliberate mistakes. Rewrite it correctly on the given stave.

7 *After* each of these notes write a *higher* note to form the named *melodic* interval. The key is C minor.

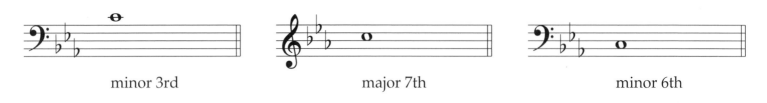

minor 3rd   major 7th   minor 6th

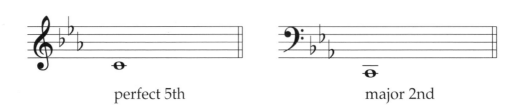

perfect 5th   major 2nd

Music Theory Past Papers 2014

ABRSM Grade 3

Theory Paper   Grade 3   2014   A

Duration 1½ hours

Candidates should answer ALL questions.
Write your answers on this paper – no others will be accepted.
Answers must be written clearly and neatly – otherwise marks may be lost.

TOTAL MARKS
100

1   Add the time signature to each of these five melodies.

10

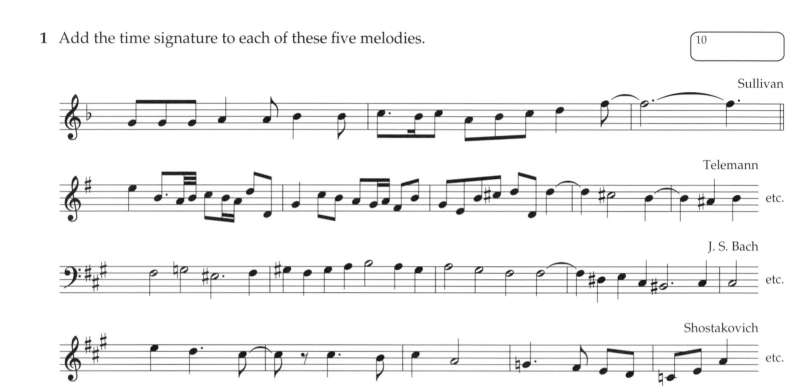

Sullivan

Telemann

J. S. Bach

Shostakovich

© Copyright 1960 by Boosey & Hawkes Music Publishers Ltd
for the UK, British Commonwealth (Ex. Canada) and Eire. Reproduced by permission.

Dvořák

2   Write a complete four-bar rhythm in $\frac{12}{8}$ time using the given opening.
   Remember to complete the first bar.

10

8 Look at this melody, which is adapted from a piece by J. F. Fasch, and then answer the questions below.

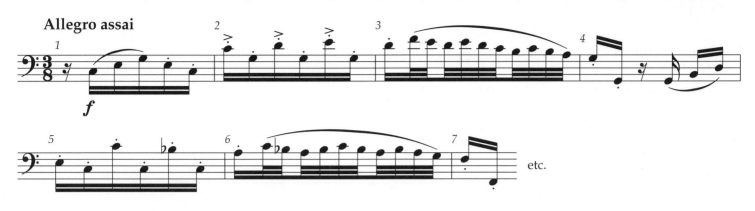

(a) Give the meaning of:

Allegro ....

assai ....

f ....

> (bar 2) ....

the dots above the notes (e.g. bar 5) ....

(b) (i) Describe the time signature as: simple or compound ....

duple, triple or quadruple ....

(ii) Give the letter name of the *highest* note in the melody. ....

(iii) The melody is in the key of C major. Draw a circle around three notes next to each other that form the tonic triad of this key.

(iv) Draw a circle around a note in bars 1–3 that is the 7th degree of the scale of C major.

(v) Give the time name (e.g. crotchet or quarter note) of the *shortest* note in the melody. ....

(c) Write out the melody from the beginning of bar 1 to the end of bar 3 using notes and a rest of *twice the value*. Remember to put in the new time signature at the place marked ∗, and remember to group (beam) the notes correctly.

∗

Theory Paper   Grade 3   2014   B

TOTAL MARKS
100

Duration 1½ hours

Candidates should answer ALL questions.
Write your answers on this paper – no others will be accepted.
Answers must be written clearly and neatly – otherwise marks may be lost.

1   (a)   Add the missing bar-lines to each of these *two* melodies, which both begin on the
first beat of the bar.

10

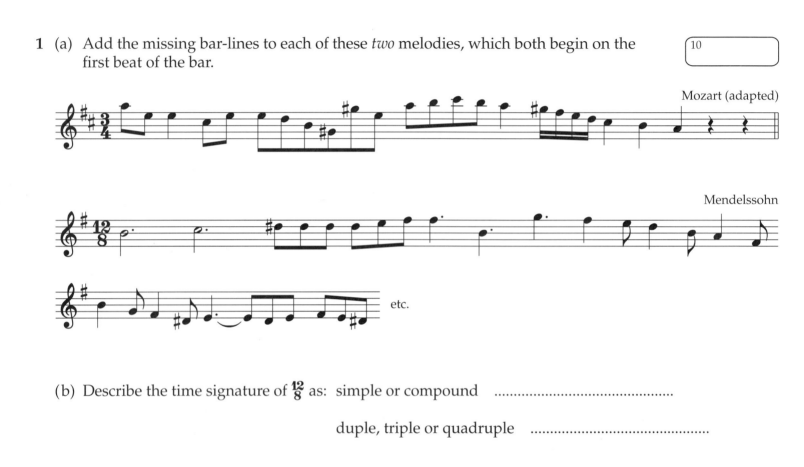

Mozart (adapted)

Mendelssohn

etc.

(b)   Describe the time signature of $\frac{12}{8}$ as: simple or compound   ....

duple, triple or quadruple   ....

2   Write a complete four-bar rhythm in $\frac{6}{8}$ time using the given opening, which begins on
an upbeat.

10

3 Describe each of these melodic intervals, giving the type and number (e.g. major 3rd, perfect 8ve). The keys are named, and in each case the lower note is the key note.

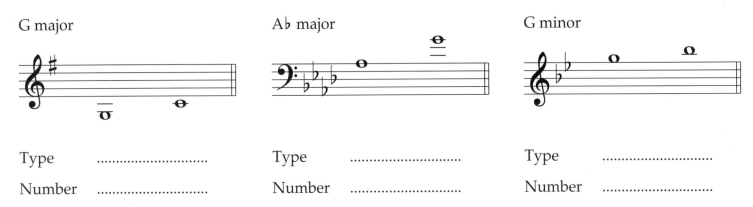

G major   Ab major   G minor

Type ....   Type ....   Type ....

Number ....   Number ....   Number ....

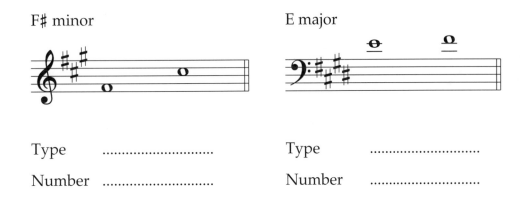

F# minor   E major

Type ....   Type ....

Number ....   Number ....

4 Add the correct rest(s) at the places marked ✳ in these two melodies to make each bar complete.

5 Transpose this melody *down* an octave, using the bass clef as shown.

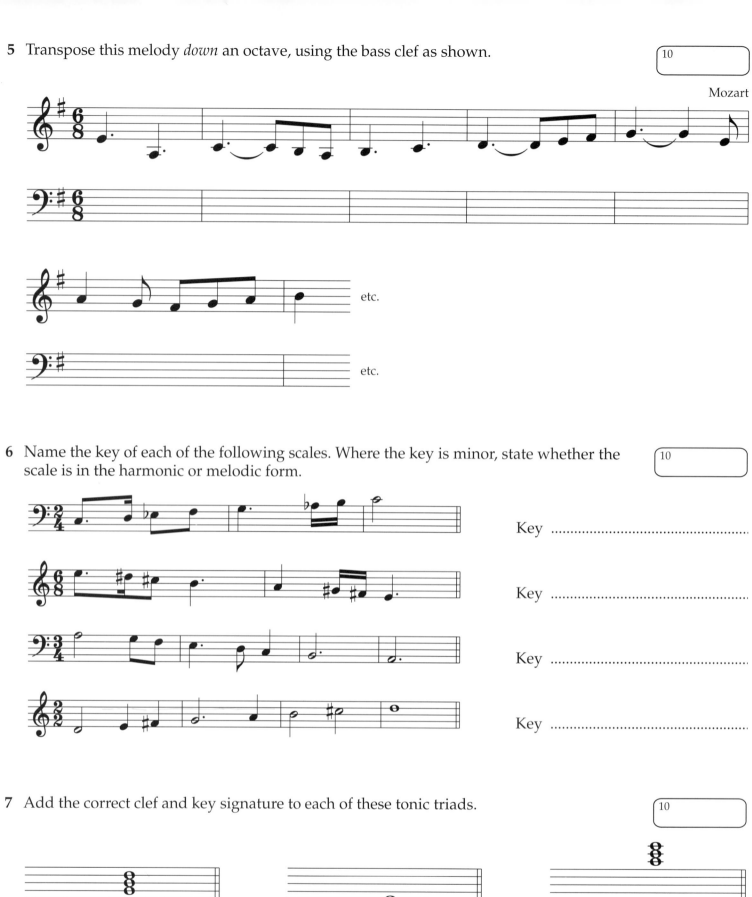

Mozart

etc.

etc.

6 Name the key of each of the following scales. Where the key is minor, state whether the scale is in the harmonic or melodic form.

Key ....

Key ....

Key ....

Key ....

7 Add the correct clef and key signature to each of these tonic triads.

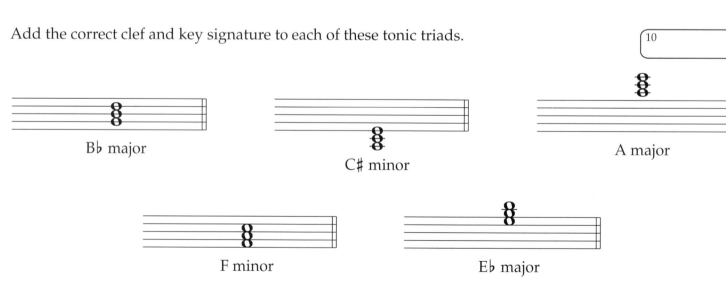

Bb major

C# minor

A major

F minor

Eb major

8 Look at this melody, which is adapted from a piece by Mendelssohn, and then answer the questions below.

(a) Give the meaning of:

[10]

maestoso ....

the **4** in **2/4** ....

ff ....

con forza ....

dim. (e.g. bar 7) ....

(b) (i) The first phrase has been marked with a square bracket ().
Mark all the other phrases in the same way.

[10]

   (ii) Complete the following statements:

   Bar 2 has the same rhythm as bar ....

   The triplet (♪♪♪ with 3) in bar 2 means three semiquavers (16th notes) in the time of

   ....

   (iii) The melody is in the key of E minor. Draw a circle around a note in this melody
   that is *not* in this key.

   (iv) Give the time name (e.g. crotchet or
   quarter note) of the *shortest* note in the melody. ....

(c) Write out the melody from the beginning of the music to the end of bar 4 in notes of
twice the value. Remember to put in the new time signature at the place marked ∗,
and remember to group (beam) the notes correctly.

[10]

Theory Paper   Grade 3   2014   C

Duration 1½ hours

Candidates should answer ALL questions.
Write your answers on this paper – no others will be accepted.
Answers must be written clearly and neatly – otherwise marks may be lost.

TOTAL MARKS
100

1   Add the missing bar-lines to each of these *two* melodies, which both begin on the first beat of the bar.

10

2   Write a complete four-bar rhythm in 4/4 time using the given opening.

10

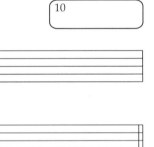

3   (a) Rewrite the following melody with the notes correctly grouped (beamed).

10

   (b) Draw a circle around two notes next to each other in the melody that are a major 3rd apart.

4 (a) Using semibreves (whole notes), write one octave **ascending** of the **melodic** minor scale that has the given key signature. Remember to include any additional sharp or flat signs. [10]

(b) Using semibreves (whole notes), write one octave **descending** of the scale of A♭ major, without key signature but including any necessary sharp or flat signs.

5 Name the key of each of these tonic triads. [10]

....

....

6 Add the correct rest(s) at the places marked ∗ in these two melodies to make each bar complete. [10]

Haydn

Berlioz

7 Rewrite this melody using notes and a rest of *half the value*. Remember to put in the new time signature at the place marked ∗, and remember to group (beam) the notes correctly. [10]

Beethoven

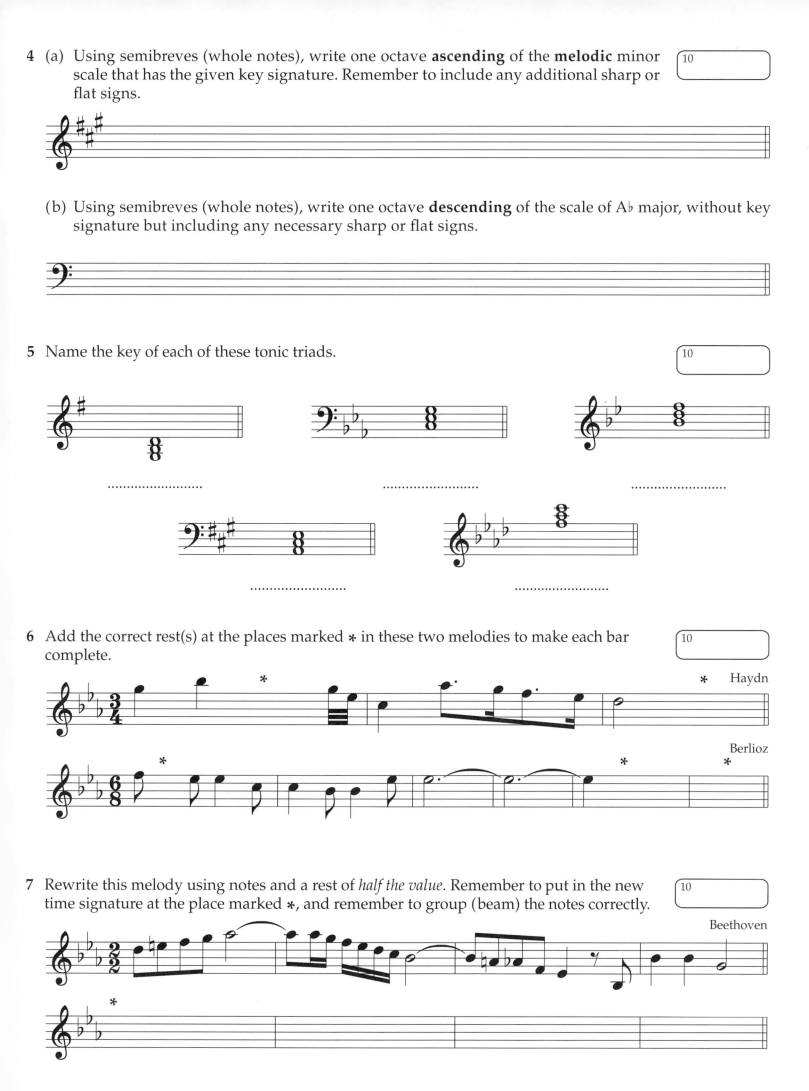

8 Look at this melody by Britten and then answer the questions below.

(a) Give the meaning of:

alla marcia ....

♩ = 108 ....

pp ....

> (e.g. bar 2) ....

⌣ (bars 3–4, marked ↑) ....

(b) (i) Name one similarity and one difference between bar 1 and bar 3.

Similarity ....

Difference ....

(ii) Which form of the scale of B minor is used in bar 2: harmonic or melodic? ....

(iii) Which other key has the same key signature as B minor? ....

(iv) Name the degree of the scale (e.g. 2nd, 3rd) of the
last note of the melody. Remember that the key is B minor. ....

(v) Answer TRUE or FALSE to this statement:

The notes in bar 1 should be played smoothly. ....

(c) Write out the whole melody *an octave lower*, using the bass clef as shown.

Theory Paper   Grade 3   2014   S

TOTAL MARKS
100

Duration 1½ hours

Candidates should answer ALL questions.
Write your answers on this paper – no others will be accepted.
Answers must be written clearly and neatly – otherwise marks may be lost.

1   Add the time signature to each of these five melodies.

10

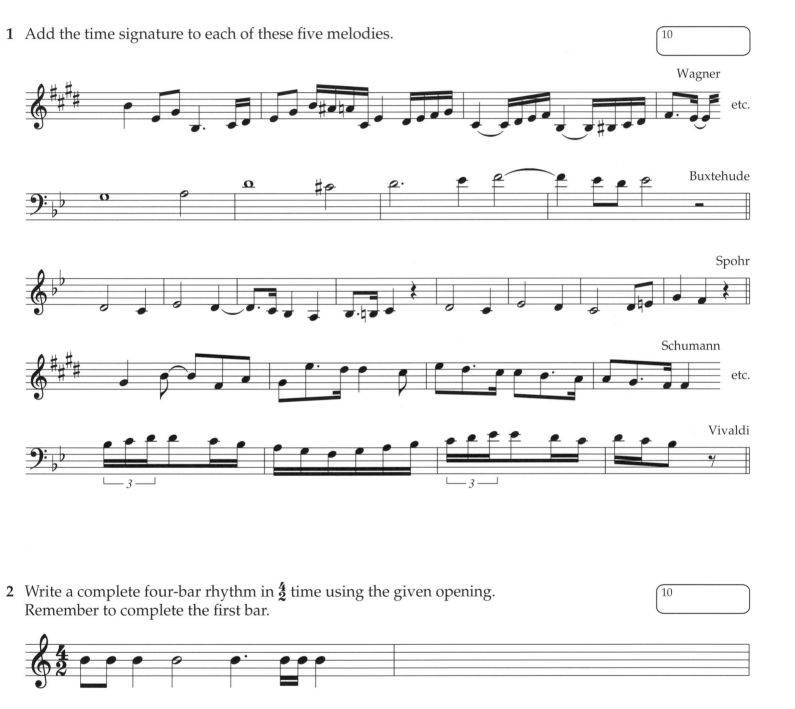

2   Write a complete four-bar rhythm in $\frac{4}{2}$ time using the given opening.
    Remember to complete the first bar.

10

3 (a) Using semibreves (whole notes), write one octave **ascending** of the scale of C **melodic** minor, with key signature. `[10]`

(b) Add the correct clef and any necessary sharp or flat signs to make the scale of E major. Do *not* use a key signature.

4 Rewrite this melody using notes of *twice the value*. Remember to put in the new time signature at the place marked **✶**, and remember to group (beam) the notes correctly. `[10]`

Telemann

etc.

✶

etc.

5 Describe each of these harmonic intervals, giving the type and number (e.g. major 2nd, perfect 8ve). The keys are named, and in each case the lower note is the key note. `[10]`

E minor

G minor

B♭ major

Type ....

Type ....

Type ....

Number ....

Number ....

Number ....

D major

F minor

Type ....

Type ....

Number ....

Number ....

14

6 Give the letter name of each of these notes. The first answer is given.

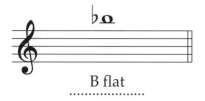

B flat
....

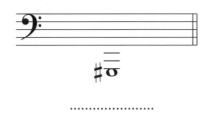

....

....

....

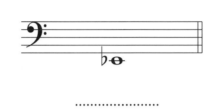

....

....

7 Rewrite the following melody with the notes correctly grouped (beamed).

J. S. Bach

8 Look at this melody by Mendelssohn and then answer the questions below.

(a) Give the meaning of:

maestoso ....

assai ....

♩. = 104 ....

sf (bar 2) ....

> (bar 5) ....

(b) (i) The melody is in the key of A major. Name the degree
of the scale (e.g. 5th, 6th) of the last note of the melody. ....

(ii) Which other key has the same key signature as A major? ....

(iii) How many semiquavers (16th notes) is the first note of bar 5 worth? ....

(iv) Answer TRUE or FALSE to this statement:

There are two pairs of tied notes in this melody. ....

(v) Describe the time signature as: simple or compound ....

duple, triple or quadruple ....

(c) Write out the melody from the beginning of bar 1 to the end of bar 4 *an octave higher*,
using the treble clef as shown.

ABRSM
24 Portland Place
London W1B 1LU
United Kingdom

www.abrsm.org

MIX
Paper from
responsible sources
FSC™ C109619

Published by ABRSM (Publishing) Ltd,
a wholly owned subsidiary of ABRSM
Cover by Kate Benjamin & Andy Potts
Printed in England by Page Bros (Norwich) Ltd

ISBN 978-1-84849-722-1

9 781848 497221